Hello Beautiful,

Are you wondering what chapter mapping is?

Chapter mapping is a methodical, intentional way of studying one book of the Bible in context, by going one chapter at a time, through the entire book.

The Bible was written by real life everyday people, about real life everyday people, to real life everyday people, and for us, real life everyday people.

As we study the Bible, we need to keep all of these factors at the forefront of our mind, looking into a book as a whole and not just pulling out a verse here and there.

To do that, we have to slow down and look into the details more carefully. The best way to do that is one chapter at a time.

By looking at the chapter as a whole, we are better noticing themes and topics that the author meant for people to notice.

The authors of the Bible, inspired by the Holy Spirit, were literary geniuses. The Bible is a beautiful literary masterpiece. If we stop to smell the roses, as the saying goes, we will find beautiful treasures along the way.

I like to call this UNFOLDING TRUTH.

We are slowly and methodically taking the layers of a biblical book and breaking them down into chapters to help us study the chapter as a whole, and therefore the book as a whole.

In this workbook there are enough chapter mapping pages to go through the Book of Genesis studying in-depth as you go, unfolding the truth of God's Word.

My sweet friend, you are opening a beautiful love letter. A love letter from God, for you.

He wants us to understand His word by finding the lessons and truths within it. Most of all, He wants us to praise Him for who He is and what He does within the pages of each book.

Looking at the chapter as a whole will help you study His word and unravel the truths and topics you were meant to notice and apply to your life.

Bible study is not all about, "What did this mean historically to the people then?" Although that is incredibly important. If you stopped there, that would just be information.

God wants us to have transformation as well, by unfolding the layers of who He is, what He has done, and what He still does today.

Answer the prompts in each box, for each chapter, as you go through the book. You will find yourself noticing themes and topics that are related to one another as you go.

As you unfold, you will start to see the whole picture: defining words, comparing translations, finding related passages, learning fun facts along the way, but most importantly you will begin to see God in a new way. You will see that nothing matters but Him and how you live your life for Him.

I like to study one chapter per week to really dig in and learn as much as I can, but you go through the book at the pace that works for you.

Happy Unfolding my friend,

CHAPTER: Note the chapter here

Make sure to write the verse references that correspond to your notes.

NOTES ON WHAT THIS CHAPTER IS ABOUT:

WHAT I READ ABOUT GOD, JESUS, HOLY SPIRIT:

Summarize what the chapter says in your own words, to help you slow down when you are reading. Carefully observing the details of each passage. By paraphrasing the chapter into your own words, you will better retain what you read. Consider color-coding all titles for God and all pronouns in place of His name here in your summary so that He stands out most to you.

Make a list specifically what is mentioned about the triune God: Father, Son, and Spirit. Note what is mentioned about Him and titles given to Him. This will help you praise Him at the end of your study.

3 Choose 2-4 keywords (important or interesting words) from the entire chapter and define them in the original language (Hebrew OT, Greek NT) and if necessary, in English too (only write it down if it is helpful).

4 Choose 2-4 words or phrases that are interesting and compare the wording that a few other translations use (only write it down if it is helpful).

5 Using the words or phrases that you looked into, research and note the verses and/or passages where the Bible speaks of the same topic or truth, in the same, or a very similar way. Only write them down if they are helpful to you.

I try to find cross references verses in the same book first, then books written by the same author. Then I look into the rest of the Bible. It's especially neat to tie the Old and New Testament together by finding verses in both places. You only want to note verses or passages that were helpful to you in understanding the chapter better. It is especially important to find cross reference verses that are about God whenever possible.

FUN FACTS I DISCOVERED:

Using a study Bible or commentary book, look at the notes for the verses that contained the words you looked into, or that contain important topics or truths, and note what the experts have to say. It is often helpful to use a few different expert opinions since they do differ at times. Write the facts that are helpful too you.

LESSONS I LEARNED FROM GOD OR THE OTHER PEOPLE:

THINGS I REALIZED THAT I NEED TO CHANGE IN MY OWN LIFE:

Did God teach the people something? Can what He taught apply to you too? Did the people handle a situation in a godly way? If not, what did you learn from them? Note it here.

Did the Holy Spirit tug at your heart about the lessons you learned based on what you learned from or about God or what the people did? If so, confess those things, and/or ask for Gods help to change those things.

PRAYER AND PRAISE BASED ON WHAT I LEARNED:

9 Share your heart with God based on the entire chapter, quoting His Word back to Him in prayer and praising Him for what you learned about Him. Thank God for who He is and What He did and/or still does today. This is all about Him, not about you, so make sure to tell Him what you learned in this chapter that will draw you closer to Him.

THE BOOK OF

Genesis

1 WHO WAS THE HUMAN AUTHOR AND WHAT DO YOU KNOW ABOUT HIM?

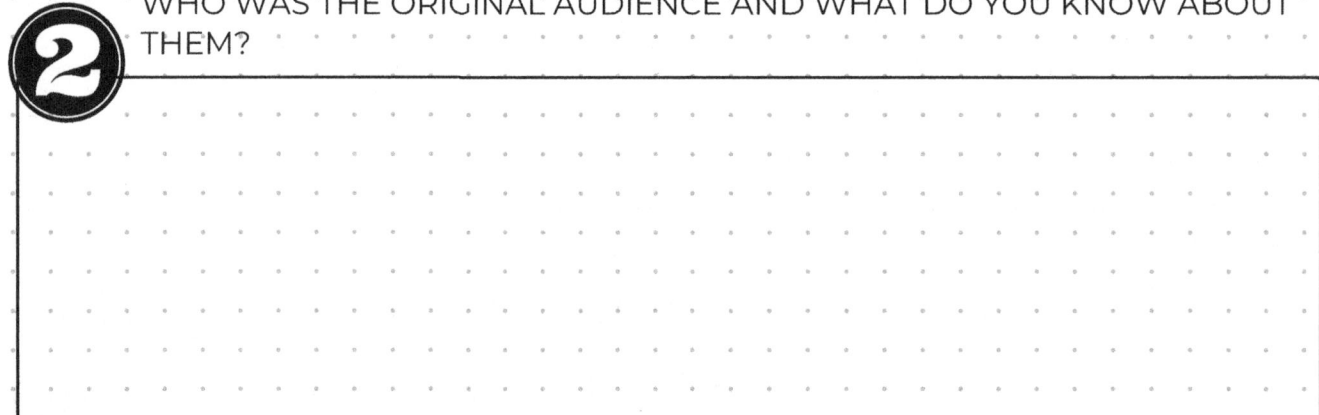

2 WHO WAS THE ORIGINAL AUDIENCE AND WHAT DO YOU KNOW ABOUT THEM?

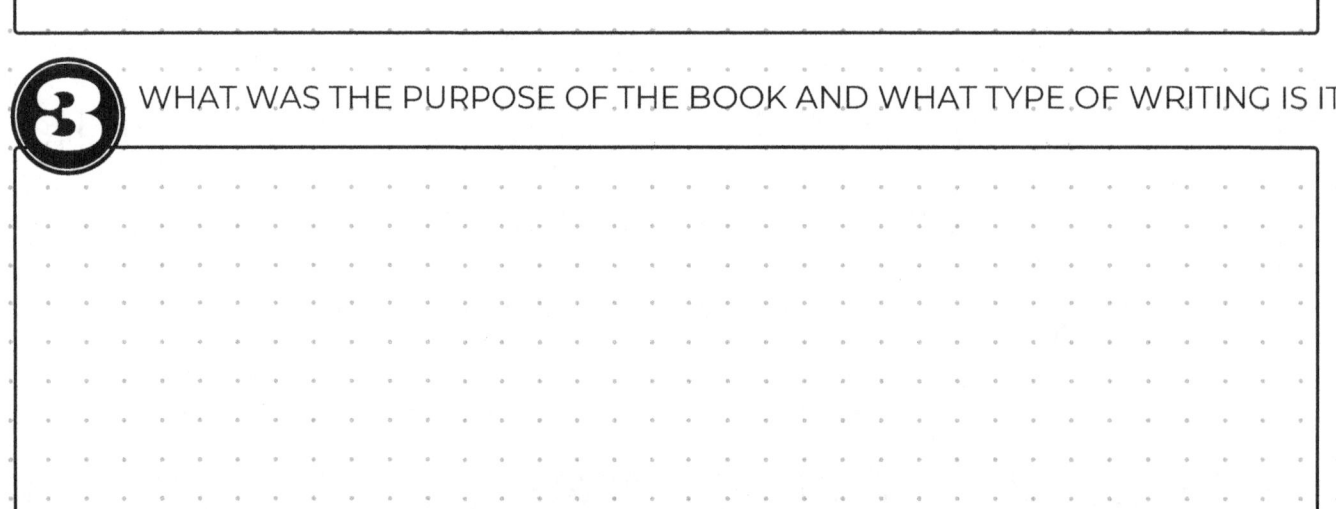

3 WHAT WAS THE PURPOSE OF THE BOOK AND WHAT TYPE OF WRITING IS IT?

WHERE WAS THE AUTHOR AT THE TIME OF WRITING AND WHAT WAS THE APPROXIMATE TIME PERIOD?

4

WHO ARE THE KEY PEOPLE OR KEY PLACES IN THIS BOOK?

5

WHAT ARE THE MAIN MESSAGES AND THEMES OF THE BOOK?

6

OTHER FUN FACTS ABOUT THIS BOOK OR AUTHOR:

7

CHAPTER:

Make sure to write the verse references that correspond to your notes.

NOTES ON WHAT THIS CHAPTER IS ABOUT:

1

WHAT I READ ABOUT GOD, JESUS, HOLY SPIRIT:

2

WORDS I DEFINED:

3

WORDS OR PHRASES I COMPARED TO OTHER BIBLE TRANSLATIONS:

4

CROSS REFERENCE VERSES THAT HELPED ME UNDERSTAND THIS BETTER:

5

CROSS REFERENCES CONT.

FUN FACTS I DISCOVERED:

6

LESSONS I LEARNED FROM GOD OR THE OTHER PEOPLE:

7

THINGS I REALIZED THAT I NEED TO CHANGE IN MY OWN LIFE:

8

PRAYER AND PRAISE BASED ON WHAT I LEARNED:

9

NOTES:

CHAPTER:

Make sure to write the verse references that correspond to your notes.

NOTES ON WHAT THIS CHAPTER IS ABOUT:

1

WHAT I READ ABOUT GOD, JESUS, HOLY SPIRIT:

2

WORDS I DEFINED:

3

WORDS OR PHRASES I COMPARED TO OTHER BIBLE TRANSLATIONS:

4

CROSS REFERENCE VERSES THAT HELPED ME UNDERSTAND THIS BETTER:

5

CROSS REFERENCES CONT.

FUN FACTS I DISCOVERED:

6

LESSONS I LEARNED FROM GOD OR THE OTHER PEOPLE:

7

THINGS I REALIZED THAT I NEED TO CHANGE IN MY OWN LIFE:

8

PRAYER AND PRAISE BASED ON WHAT I LEARNED:

9

NOTES:

CHAPTER:

Make sure to write the verse references that correspond to your notes.

NOTES ON WHAT THIS CHAPTER IS ABOUT:

1

WHAT I READ ABOUT GOD, JESUS, HOLY SPIRIT:

2

WORDS I DEFINED:

3

WORDS OR PHRASES I COMPARED TO
OTHER BIBLE TRANSLATIONS:

4

CROSS REFERENCE VERSES THAT HELPED ME UNDERSTAND THIS BETTER:

5

CROSS REFERENCES CONT.

FUN FACTS I DISCOVERED:

6

LESSONS I LEARNED FROM GOD OR
THE OTHER PEOPLE:

7

THINGS I REALIZED THAT I NEED TO
CHANGE IN MY OWN LIFE:

8

PRAYER AND PRAISE BASED ON WHAT I LEARNED:

9

NOTES:

CHAPTER:

Make sure to write the verse references that correspond to your notes.

NOTES ON WHAT THIS CHAPTER IS ABOUT:

1

WHAT I READ ABOUT GOD, JESUS, HOLY SPIRIT:

2

WORDS I DEFINED:

3

WORDS OR PHRASES I COMPARED TO
OTHER BIBLE TRANSLATIONS:

4

CROSS REFERENCE VERSES THAT HELPED ME UNDERSTAND THIS BETTER:

5

CROSS REFERENCES CONT.

FUN FACTS I DISCOVERED:

6

LESSONS I LEARNED FROM GOD OR
THE OTHER PEOPLE:

7

THINGS I REALIZED THAT I NEED TO
CHANGE IN MY OWN LIFE:

8

PRAYER AND PRAISE BASED ON WHAT I LEARNED:

9

NOTES:

CHAPTER:

Make sure to write the verse references that correspond to your notes.

NOTES ON WHAT THIS CHAPTER IS ABOUT:

1

WHAT I READ ABOUT GOD, JESUS, HOLY SPIRIT:

2

WORDS I DEFINED:

3

WORDS OR PHRASES I COMPARED TO OTHER BIBLE TRANSLATIONS:

4

CROSS REFERENCE VERSES THAT HELPED ME UNDERSTAND THIS BETTER:

5

CROSS REFERENCES CONT.

FUN FACTS I DISCOVERED:

6

LESSONS I LEARNED FROM GOD OR THE OTHER PEOPLE:

7

THINGS I REALIZED THAT I NEED TO CHANGE IN MY OWN LIFE:

8

PRAYER AND PRAISE BASED ON WHAT I LEARNED:

9

NOTES:

CHAPTER:

Make sure to write the verse references that correspond to your notes.

NOTES ON WHAT THIS CHAPTER IS ABOUT:

1

WHAT I READ ABOUT GOD, JESUS, HOLY SPIRIT:

2

WORDS I DEFINED:

3

WORDS OR PHRASES I COMPARED TO
OTHER BIBLE TRANSLATIONS:

4

CROSS REFERENCE VERSES THAT HELPED ME UNDERSTAND THIS BETTER:

5

CROSS REFERENCES CONT.

FUN FACTS I DISCOVERED:

6

LESSONS I LEARNED FROM GOD OR
THE OTHER PEOPLE:

7

THINGS I REALIZED THAT I NEED TO
CHANGE IN MY OWN LIFE:

8

PRAYER AND PRAISE BASED ON WHAT I LEARNED:

9

NOTES:

CHAPTER:

Make sure to write the verse references that correspond to your notes.

NOTES ON WHAT THIS CHAPTER IS ABOUT:

1

WHAT I READ ABOUT GOD,
JESUS, HOLY SPIRIT:

2

WORDS I DEFINED:

3

WORDS OR PHRASES I COMPARED TO OTHER BIBLE TRANSLATIONS:

4

CROSS REFERENCE VERSES THAT HELPED ME UNDERSTAND THIS BETTER:

5

CROSS REFERENCES CONT.

FUN FACTS I DISCOVERED:

6

LESSONS I LEARNED FROM GOD OR THE OTHER PEOPLE:

7

THINGS I REALIZED THAT I NEED TO CHANGE IN MY OWN LIFE:

8

PRAYER AND PRAISE BASED ON WHAT I LEARNED:

9

NOTES:

CHAPTER:

Make sure to write the verse references that correspond to your notes.

NOTES ON WHAT THIS CHAPTER IS ABOUT:

1

WHAT I READ ABOUT GOD, JESUS, HOLY SPIRIT:

2

WORDS I DEFINED:

③

WORDS OR PHRASES I COMPARED TO OTHER BIBLE TRANSLATIONS:

④

CROSS REFERENCE VERSES THAT HELPED ME UNDERSTAND THIS BETTER:

⑤

CROSS REFERENCES CONT.

FUN FACTS I DISCOVERED:

6

LESSONS I LEARNED FROM GOD OR
THE OTHER PEOPLE:

7

THINGS I REALIZED THAT I NEED TO
CHANGE IN MY OWN LIFE:

8

PRAYER AND PRAISE BASED ON WHAT I LEARNED:

9

NOTES:

CHAPTER:

Make sure to write the verse references that correspond to your notes.

NOTES ON WHAT THIS CHAPTER IS ABOUT:

1

WHAT I READ ABOUT GOD, JESUS, HOLY SPIRIT:

2

WORDS I DEFINED:

3

WORDS OR PHRASES I COMPARED TO OTHER BIBLE TRANSLATIONS:

4

CROSS REFERENCE VERSES THAT HELPED ME UNDERSTAND THIS BETTER:

5

CROSS REFERENCES CONT.

FUN FACTS I DISCOVERED:

6

LESSONS I LEARNED FROM GOD OR
THE OTHER PEOPLE:

7

THINGS I REALIZED THAT I NEED TO
CHANGE IN MY OWN LIFE:

8

PRAYER AND PRAISE BASED ON WHAT I LEARNED:

9

NOTES:

CHAPTER:

Make sure to write the verse references that correspond to your notes.

NOTES ON WHAT THIS CHAPTER IS ABOUT:

1

WHAT I READ ABOUT GOD, JESUS, HOLY SPIRIT:

2

WORDS I DEFINED:

3

WORDS OR PHRASES I COMPARED TO OTHER BIBLE TRANSLATIONS:

4

CROSS REFERENCE VERSES THAT HELPED ME UNDERSTAND THIS BETTER:

5

CROSS REFERENCES CONT.

FUN FACTS I DISCOVERED:

6

LESSONS I LEARNED FROM GOD OR
THE OTHER PEOPLE:

7

THINGS I REALIZED THAT I NEED TO
CHANGE IN MY OWN LIFE:

8

PRAYER AND PRAISE BASED ON WHAT I LEARNED:

9

NOTES:

CHAPTER:

Make sure to write the verse references that correspond to your notes.

NOTES ON WHAT THIS CHAPTER IS ABOUT:

1

WHAT I READ ABOUT GOD, JESUS, HOLY SPIRIT:

2

WORDS I DEFINED:

3

WORDS OR PHRASES I COMPARED TO OTHER BIBLE TRANSLATIONS:

4

CROSS REFERENCE VERSES THAT HELPED ME UNDERSTAND THIS BETTER:

5

CROSS REFERENCES CONT.

FUN FACTS I DISCOVERED:

6

LESSONS I LEARNED FROM GOD OR THE OTHER PEOPLE:

7

THINGS I REALIZED THAT I NEED TO CHANGE IN MY OWN LIFE:

8

PRAYER AND PRAISE BASED ON WHAT I LEARNED:

9

NOTES:

CHAPTER:

Make sure to write the verse references that correspond to your notes.

NOTES ON WHAT THIS CHAPTER IS ABOUT:

1

WHAT I READ ABOUT GOD, JESUS, HOLY SPIRIT:

2

WORDS I DEFINED:

3

WORDS OR PHRASES I COMPARED TO OTHER BIBLE TRANSLATIONS:

4

CROSS REFERENCE VERSES THAT HELPED ME UNDERSTAND THIS BETTER:

5

CROSS REFERENCES CONT.

FUN FACTS I DISCOVERED:

6

LESSONS I LEARNED FROM GOD OR
THE OTHER PEOPLE:

7

THINGS I REALIZED THAT I NEED TO
CHANGE IN MY OWN LIFE:

8

PRAYER AND PRAISE BASED ON WHAT I LEARNED:

9

NOTES:

CHAPTER:

Make sure to write the verse references that correspond to your notes.

NOTES ON WHAT THIS CHAPTER IS ABOUT:

1

WHAT I READ ABOUT GOD, JESUS, HOLY SPIRIT:

2

WORDS I DEFINED:

3

WORDS OR PHRASES I COMPARED TO OTHER BIBLE TRANSLATIONS:

4

CROSS REFERENCE VERSES THAT HELPED ME UNDERSTAND THIS BETTER:

5

CROSS REFERENCES CONT.

FUN FACTS I DISCOVERED:

6

LESSONS I LEARNED FROM GOD OR
THE OTHER PEOPLE:

7

THINGS I REALIZED THAT I NEED TO
CHANGE IN MY OWN LIFE:

8

PRAYER AND PRAISE BASED ON WHAT I LEARNED:

9

NOTES:

CHAPTER:

Make sure to write the verse references that correspond to your notes.

NOTES ON WHAT THIS CHAPTER IS ABOUT:

1

WHAT I READ ABOUT GOD, JESUS, HOLY SPIRIT:

2

WORDS I DEFINED:

3

WORDS OR PHRASES I COMPARED TO OTHER BIBLE TRANSLATIONS:

4

CROSS REFERENCE VERSES THAT HELPED ME UNDERSTAND THIS BETTER:

5

CROSS REFERENCES CONT.

FUN FACTS I DISCOVERED:

6

LESSONS I LEARNED FROM GOD OR THE OTHER PEOPLE:

7

THINGS I REALIZED THAT I NEED TO CHANGE IN MY OWN LIFE:

8

PRAYER AND PRAISE BASED ON WHAT I LEARNED:

9

NOTES:

CHAPTER:

Make sure to write the verse references that correspond to your notes.

NOTES ON WHAT THIS CHAPTER IS ABOUT:

1

WHAT I READ ABOUT GOD, JESUS, HOLY SPIRIT:

2

WORDS I DEFINED:

3

WORDS OR PHRASES I COMPARED TO OTHER BIBLE TRANSLATIONS:

4

CROSS REFERENCE VERSES THAT HELPED ME UNDERSTAND THIS BETTER:

5

CROSS REFERENCES CONT.

FUN FACTS I DISCOVERED:

6

LESSONS I LEARNED FROM GOD OR THE OTHER PEOPLE:

7

THINGS I REALIZED THAT I NEED TO CHANGE IN MY OWN LIFE:

8

PRAYER AND PRAISE BASED ON WHAT I LEARNED:

9

NOTES:

CHAPTER:

Make sure to write the verse references that correspond to your notes.

NOTES ON WHAT THIS CHAPTER IS ABOUT:

1

WHAT I READ ABOUT GOD, JESUS, HOLY SPIRIT:

2

WORDS I DEFINED:

3

WORDS OR PHRASES I COMPARED TO OTHER BIBLE TRANSLATIONS:

4

CROSS REFERENCE VERSES THAT HELPED ME UNDERSTAND THIS BETTER:

5

CROSS REFERENCES CONT.

FUN FACTS I DISCOVERED:

6

LESSONS I LEARNED FROM GOD OR
THE OTHER PEOPLE:

7

THINGS I REALIZED THAT I NEED TO
CHANGE IN MY OWN LIFE:

8

PRAYER AND PRAISE BASED ON WHAT I LEARNED:

9

NOTES:

CHAPTER:

Make sure to write the verse references that correspond to your notes.

NOTES ON WHAT THIS CHAPTER IS ABOUT:

1

WHAT I READ ABOUT GOD, JESUS, HOLY SPIRIT:

2

WORDS I DEFINED:

3

WORDS OR PHRASES I COMPARED TO OTHER BIBLE TRANSLATIONS:

4

CROSS REFERENCE VERSES THAT HELPED ME UNDERSTAND THIS BETTER:

5

CROSS REFERENCES CONT.

FUN FACTS I DISCOVERED:

6

LESSONS I LEARNED FROM GOD OR THE OTHER PEOPLE:

7

THINGS I REALIZED THAT I NEED TO CHANGE IN MY OWN LIFE:

8

PRAYER AND PRAISE BASED ON WHAT I LEARNED:

9

NOTES:

CHAPTER:

Make sure to write the verse references that correspond to your notes.

NOTES ON WHAT THIS CHAPTER IS ABOUT:

1

WHAT I READ ABOUT GOD,
JESUS, HOLY SPIRIT:

2

WORDS I DEFINED:

3

WORDS OR PHRASES I COMPARED TO OTHER BIBLE TRANSLATIONS:

4

CROSS REFERENCE VERSES THAT HELPED ME UNDERSTAND THIS BETTER:

5

CROSS REFERENCES CONT.

FUN FACTS I DISCOVERED:

6

LESSONS I LEARNED FROM GOD OR
THE OTHER PEOPLE:

7

THINGS I REALIZED THAT I NEED TO
CHANGE IN MY OWN LIFE:

8

PRAYER AND PRAISE BASED ON WHAT I LEARNED:

9

NOTES:

CHAPTER:

Make sure to write the verse references that correspond to your notes.

NOTES ON WHAT THIS CHAPTER IS ABOUT:

1

WHAT I READ ABOUT GOD, JESUS, HOLY SPIRIT:

2

WORDS I DEFINED:

3

WORDS OR PHRASES I COMPARED TO OTHER BIBLE TRANSLATIONS:

4

CROSS REFERENCE VERSES THAT HELPED ME UNDERSTAND THIS BETTER:

5

CROSS REFERENCES CONT.

FUN FACTS I DISCOVERED:

6

LESSONS I LEARNED FROM GOD OR
THE OTHER PEOPLE:

7

THINGS I REALIZED THAT I NEED TO
CHANGE IN MY OWN LIFE:

8

PRAYER AND PRAISE BASED ON WHAT I LEARNED:

9

NOTES:

CHAPTER:

Make sure to write the verse references that correspond to your notes.

NOTES ON WHAT THIS CHAPTER IS ABOUT:

1

WHAT I READ ABOUT GOD, JESUS, HOLY SPIRIT:

2

WORDS I DEFINED:

3

WORDS OR PHRASES I COMPARED TO OTHER BIBLE TRANSLATIONS:

4

CROSS REFERENCE VERSES THAT HELPED ME UNDERSTAND THIS BETTER:

5

CROSS REFERENCES CONT.

FUN FACTS I DISCOVERED:

6

LESSONS I LEARNED FROM GOD OR THE OTHER PEOPLE:

7

THINGS I REALIZED THAT I NEED TO CHANGE IN MY OWN LIFE:

8

PRAYER AND PRAISE BASED ON WHAT I LEARNED:

9

NOTES:

CHAPTER:

Make sure to write the verse references that correspond to your notes.

NOTES ON WHAT THIS CHAPTER IS ABOUT:

1

WHAT I READ ABOUT GOD, JESUS, HOLY SPIRIT:

2

WORDS I DEFINED:

3

WORDS OR PHRASES I COMPARED TO OTHER BIBLE TRANSLATIONS:

4

CROSS REFERENCE VERSES THAT HELPED ME UNDERSTAND THIS BETTER:

5

CROSS REFERENCES CONT.

FUN FACTS I DISCOVERED:

6

LESSONS I LEARNED FROM GOD OR
THE OTHER PEOPLE:

7

THINGS I REALIZED THAT I NEED TO
CHANGE IN MY OWN LIFE:

8

PRAYER AND PRAISE BASED ON WHAT I LEARNED:

9

NOTES:

CHAPTER:

Make sure to write the verse references that correspond to your notes.

NOTES ON WHAT THIS CHAPTER IS ABOUT:

1

WHAT I READ ABOUT GOD,
JESUS, HOLY SPIRIT:

2

WORDS I DEFINED:

3

WORDS OR PHRASES I COMPARED TO OTHER BIBLE TRANSLATIONS:

4

CROSS REFERENCE VERSES THAT HELPED ME UNDERSTAND THIS BETTER:

5

CROSS REFERENCES CONT.

FUN FACTS I DISCOVERED:

6

LESSONS I LEARNED FROM GOD OR
THE OTHER PEOPLE:

7

THINGS I REALIZED THAT I NEED TO
CHANGE IN MY OWN LIFE:

8

PRAYER AND PRAISE BASED ON WHAT I LEARNED:

9

NOTES:

CHAPTER:

Make sure to write the verse references that correspond to your notes.

NOTES ON WHAT THIS CHAPTER IS ABOUT:

1

WHAT I READ ABOUT GOD, JESUS, HOLY SPIRIT:

2

WORDS I DEFINED:

3

WORDS OR PHRASES I COMPARED TO OTHER BIBLE TRANSLATIONS:

4

CROSS REFERENCE VERSES THAT HELPED ME UNDERSTAND THIS BETTER:

5

CROSS REFERENCES CONT.

FUN FACTS I DISCOVERED:

6

LESSONS I LEARNED FROM GOD OR THE OTHER PEOPLE:

7

THINGS I REALIZED THAT I NEED TO CHANGE IN MY OWN LIFE:

8

PRAYER AND PRAISE BASED ON WHAT I LEARNED:

9

NOTES:

CHAPTER:

Make sure to write the verse references that correspond to your notes.

NOTES ON WHAT THIS CHAPTER IS ABOUT:

1

WHAT I READ ABOUT GOD, JESUS, HOLY SPIRIT:

2

WORDS I DEFINED:

3

WORDS OR PHRASES I COMPARED TO OTHER BIBLE TRANSLATIONS:

4

CROSS REFERENCE VERSES THAT HELPED ME UNDERSTAND THIS BETTER:

5

CROSS REFERENCES CONT.

FUN FACTS I DISCOVERED:

6

LESSONS I LEARNED FROM GOD OR
THE OTHER PEOPLE:

7

THINGS I REALIZED THAT I NEED TO
CHANGE IN MY OWN LIFE:

8

PRAYER AND PRAISE BASED ON WHAT I LEARNED:

9

NOTES:

CHAPTER:

Make sure to write the verse references that correspond to your notes.

NOTES ON WHAT THIS CHAPTER IS ABOUT:

WHAT I READ ABOUT GOD, JESUS, HOLY SPIRIT:

1

2

WORDS I DEFINED:

3

WORDS OR PHRASES I COMPARED TO OTHER BIBLE TRANSLATIONS:

4

CROSS REFERENCE VERSES THAT HELPED ME UNDERSTAND THIS BETTER:

5

CROSS REFERENCES CONT.

FUN FACTS I DISCOVERED:

6

LESSONS I LEARNED FROM GOD OR THE OTHER PEOPLE:

7

THINGS I REALIZED THAT I NEED TO CHANGE IN MY OWN LIFE:

8

PRAYER AND PRAISE BASED ON WHAT I LEARNED:

9

NOTES:

CHAPTER:

Make sure to write the verse references that correspond to your notes.

NOTES ON WHAT THIS CHAPTER IS ABOUT:

1

WHAT I READ ABOUT GOD, JESUS, HOLY SPIRIT:

2

WORDS I DEFINED:

3

WORDS OR PHRASES I COMPARED TO OTHER BIBLE TRANSLATIONS:

4

CROSS REFERENCE VERSES THAT HELPED ME UNDERSTAND THIS BETTER:

5

CROSS REFERENCES CONT.

FUN FACTS I DISCOVERED:

6

LESSONS I LEARNED FROM GOD OR THE OTHER PEOPLE:

7

THINGS I REALIZED THAT I NEED TO CHANGE IN MY OWN LIFE:

8

PRAYER AND PRAISE BASED ON WHAT I LEARNED:

9

NOTES:

CHAPTER:

Make sure to write the verse references that correspond to your notes.

NOTES ON WHAT THIS CHAPTER IS ABOUT:

1

WHAT I READ ABOUT GOD, JESUS, HOLY SPIRIT:

2

WORDS I DEFINED:

3

WORDS OR PHRASES I COMPARED TO OTHER BIBLE TRANSLATIONS:

4

CROSS REFERENCE VERSES THAT HELPED ME UNDERSTAND THIS BETTER:

5

CROSS REFERENCES CONT.

FUN FACTS I DISCOVERED:

6

LESSONS I LEARNED FROM GOD OR
THE OTHER PEOPLE:

7

THINGS I REALIZED THAT I NEED TO
CHANGE IN MY OWN LIFE:

8

PRAYER AND PRAISE BASED ON WHAT I LEARNED:

9

NOTES:

CHAPTER:

Make sure to write the verse references that correspond to your notes.

NOTES ON WHAT THIS CHAPTER IS ABOUT:

1

WHAT I READ ABOUT GOD, JESUS, HOLY SPIRIT:

2

WORDS I DEFINED:

3

WORDS OR PHRASES I COMPARED TO
OTHER BIBLE TRANSLATIONS:

4

CROSS REFERENCE VERSES THAT HELPED ME UNDERSTAND THIS BETTER:

5

CROSS REFERENCES CONT.

FUN FACTS I DISCOVERED:

6

LESSONS I LEARNED FROM GOD OR
THE OTHER PEOPLE:

7

THINGS I REALIZED THAT I NEED TO
CHANGE IN MY OWN LIFE:

8

PRAYER AND PRAISE BASED ON WHAT I LEARNED:

9

NOTES:

CHAPTER:

Make sure to write the verse references that correspond to your notes.

NOTES ON WHAT THIS CHAPTER IS ABOUT:

1

WHAT I READ ABOUT GOD,
JESUS, HOLY SPIRIT:

2

WORDS I DEFINED:

3

WORDS OR PHRASES I COMPARED TO OTHER BIBLE TRANSLATIONS:

4

CROSS REFERENCE VERSES THAT HELPED ME UNDERSTAND THIS BETTER:

5

CROSS REFERENCES CONT.

FUN FACTS I DISCOVERED:

6

LESSONS I LEARNED FROM GOD OR
THE OTHER PEOPLE:

7

THINGS I REALIZED THAT I NEED TO
CHANGE IN MY OWN LIFE:

8

PRAYER AND PRAISE BASED ON WHAT I LEARNED:

9

NOTES:

CHAPTER:

Make sure to write the verse references that correspond to your notes.

NOTES ON WHAT THIS CHAPTER IS ABOUT:

1

WHAT I READ ABOUT GOD, JESUS, HOLY SPIRIT:

2

WORDS I DEFINED:

3

WORDS OR PHRASES I COMPARED TO
OTHER BIBLE TRANSLATIONS:

4

CROSS REFERENCE VERSES THAT HELPED ME UNDERSTAND THIS BETTER:

5

CROSS REFERENCES CONT.

FUN FACTS I DISCOVERED:

6

LESSONS I LEARNED FROM GOD OR
THE OTHER PEOPLE:

7

THINGS I REALIZED THAT I NEED TO
CHANGE IN MY OWN LIFE:

8

PRAYER AND PRAISE BASED ON WHAT I LEARNED:

9

NOTES:

CHAPTER:

Make sure to write the verse references that correspond to your notes.

NOTES ON WHAT THIS CHAPTER IS ABOUT:

1

WHAT I READ ABOUT GOD, JESUS, HOLY SPIRIT:

2

WORDS I DEFINED:

3

WORDS OR PHRASES I COMPARED TO OTHER BIBLE TRANSLATIONS:

4

CROSS REFERENCE VERSES THAT HELPED ME UNDERSTAND THIS BETTER:

5

CROSS REFERENCES CONT.

FUN FACTS I DISCOVERED:

6

LESSONS I LEARNED FROM GOD OR
THE OTHER PEOPLE:

7

THINGS I REALIZED THAT I NEED TO
CHANGE IN MY OWN LIFE:

8

PRAYER AND PRAISE BASED ON WHAT I LEARNED:

9

NOTES:

CHAPTER:

Make sure to write the verse references that correspond to your notes.

NOTES ON WHAT THIS CHAPTER IS ABOUT:

1

WHAT I READ ABOUT GOD, JESUS, HOLY SPIRIT:

2

WORDS I DEFINED:

3

WORDS OR PHRASES I COMPARED TO
OTHER BIBLE TRANSLATIONS:

4

CROSS REFERENCE VERSES THAT HELPED ME UNDERSTAND THIS BETTER:

5

CROSS REFERENCES CONT.

FUN FACTS I DISCOVERED:

6

LESSONS I LEARNED FROM GOD OR
THE OTHER PEOPLE:

7

THINGS I REALIZED THAT I NEED TO
CHANGE IN MY OWN LIFE:

8

PRAYER AND PRAISE BASED ON WHAT I LEARNED:

9

NOTES:

CHAPTER:

Make sure to write the verse references that correspond to your notes.

NOTES ON WHAT THIS CHAPTER IS ABOUT:

1

WHAT I READ ABOUT GOD, JESUS, HOLY SPIRIT:

2

WORDS I DEFINED:

3

WORDS OR PHRASES I COMPARED TO OTHER BIBLE TRANSLATIONS:

4

CROSS REFERENCE VERSES THAT HELPED ME UNDERSTAND THIS BETTER:

5

CROSS REFERENCES CONT.

FUN FACTS I DISCOVERED:

6

LESSONS I LEARNED FROM GOD OR THE OTHER PEOPLE:

7

THINGS I REALIZED THAT I NEED TO CHANGE IN MY OWN LIFE:

8

PRAYER AND PRAISE BASED ON WHAT I LEARNED:

9

NOTES:

CHAPTER:

Make sure to write the verse references that correspond to your notes.

NOTES ON WHAT THIS CHAPTER IS ABOUT:

1

WHAT I READ ABOUT GOD, JESUS, HOLY SPIRIT:

2

WORDS I DEFINED:

3

WORDS OR PHRASES I COMPARED TO OTHER BIBLE TRANSLATIONS:

4

CROSS REFERENCE VERSES THAT HELPED ME UNDERSTAND THIS BETTER:

5

CROSS REFERENCES CONT.

FUN FACTS I DISCOVERED:

6

LESSONS I LEARNED FROM GOD OR THE OTHER PEOPLE:

7

THINGS I REALIZED THAT I NEED TO CHANGE IN MY OWN LIFE:

8

PRAYER AND PRAISE BASED ON WHAT I LEARNED:

9

NOTES:

CHAPTER:

Make sure to write the verse references that correspond to your notes.

NOTES ON WHAT THIS CHAPTER IS ABOUT:

1

WHAT I READ ABOUT GOD,
JESUS, HOLY SPIRIT:

2

WORDS I DEFINED:

3

WORDS OR PHRASES I COMPARED TO OTHER BIBLE TRANSLATIONS:

4

CROSS REFERENCE VERSES THAT HELPED ME UNDERSTAND THIS BETTER:

5

CROSS REFERENCES CONT.

FUN FACTS I DISCOVERED:

6

LESSONS I LEARNED FROM GOD OR
THE OTHER PEOPLE:

7

THINGS I REALIZED THAT I NEED TO
CHANGE IN MY OWN LIFE:

8

PRAYER AND PRAISE BASED ON WHAT I LEARNED:

9

NOTES:

CHAPTER:

Make sure to write the verse references that correspond to your notes.

NOTES ON WHAT THIS CHAPTER IS ABOUT:

1

WHAT I READ ABOUT GOD, JESUS, HOLY SPIRIT:

2

WORDS I DEFINED:

3

WORDS OR PHRASES I COMPARED TO OTHER BIBLE TRANSLATIONS:

4

CROSS REFERENCE VERSES THAT HELPED ME UNDERSTAND THIS BETTER:

5

CROSS REFERENCES CONT.

FUN FACTS I DISCOVERED:

6

LESSONS I LEARNED FROM GOD OR
THE OTHER PEOPLE:

7

THINGS I REALIZED THAT I NEED TO
CHANGE IN MY OWN LIFE:

8

PRAYER AND PRAISE BASED ON WHAT I LEARNED:

9

NOTES:

CHAPTER:

Make sure to write the verse references that correspond to your notes.

NOTES ON WHAT THIS CHAPTER IS ABOUT:

1

WHAT I READ ABOUT GOD, JESUS, HOLY SPIRIT:

2

WORDS I DEFINED:

3

WORDS OR PHRASES I COMPARED TO OTHER BIBLE TRANSLATIONS:

4

CROSS REFERENCE VERSES THAT HELPED ME UNDERSTAND THIS BETTER:

5

CROSS REFERENCES CONT.

FUN FACTS I DISCOVERED:

6

LESSONS I LEARNED FROM GOD OR THE OTHER PEOPLE:

7

THINGS I REALIZED THAT I NEED TO CHANGE IN MY OWN LIFE:

8

PRAYER AND PRAISE BASED ON WHAT I LEARNED:

9

NOTES:

CHAPTER:

Make sure to write the verse references that correspond to your notes.

NOTES ON WHAT THIS CHAPTER IS ABOUT:

1

WHAT I READ ABOUT GOD, JESUS, HOLY SPIRIT:

2

WORDS I DEFINED:

3

WORDS OR PHRASES I COMPARED TO OTHER BIBLE TRANSLATIONS:

4

CROSS REFERENCE VERSES THAT HELPED ME UNDERSTAND THIS BETTER:

5

CROSS REFERENCES CONT.

FUN FACTS I DISCOVERED:

6

LESSONS I LEARNED FROM GOD OR THE OTHER PEOPLE:

7

THINGS I REALIZED THAT I NEED TO CHANGE IN MY OWN LIFE:

8

PRAYER AND PRAISE BASED ON WHAT I LEARNED:

9

NOTES:

CHAPTER:

Make sure to write the verse references that correspond to your notes.

NOTES ON WHAT THIS CHAPTER IS ABOUT:

1

WHAT I READ ABOUT GOD, JESUS, HOLY SPIRIT:

2

WORDS I DEFINED:

3

WORDS OR PHRASES I COMPARED TO OTHER BIBLE TRANSLATIONS:

4

CROSS REFERENCE VERSES THAT HELPED ME UNDERSTAND THIS BETTER:

5

CROSS REFERENCES CONT.

FUN FACTS I DISCOVERED:

6

LESSONS I LEARNED FROM GOD OR THE OTHER PEOPLE:

7

THINGS I REALIZED THAT I NEED TO CHANGE IN MY OWN LIFE:

8

PRAYER AND PRAISE BASED ON WHAT I LEARNED:

9

NOTES:

CHAPTER:

Make sure to write the verse references that correspond to your notes.

NOTES ON WHAT THIS CHAPTER IS ABOUT:

1

WHAT I READ ABOUT GOD, JESUS, HOLY SPIRIT:

2

WORDS I DEFINED:

3

WORDS OR PHRASES I COMPARED TO OTHER BIBLE TRANSLATIONS:

4

CROSS REFERENCE VERSES THAT HELPED ME UNDERSTAND THIS BETTER:

5

CROSS REFERENCES CONT.

FUN FACTS I DISCOVERED:

6

LESSONS I LEARNED FROM GOD OR THE OTHER PEOPLE:

7

THINGS I REALIZED THAT I NEED TO CHANGE IN MY OWN LIFE:

8

PRAYER AND PRAISE BASED ON WHAT I LEARNED:

9

NOTES:

CHAPTER:

Make sure to write the verse references that correspond to your notes.

NOTES ON WHAT THIS CHAPTER IS ABOUT:

1

WHAT I READ ABOUT GOD, JESUS, HOLY SPIRIT:

2

WORDS I DEFINED:

3

WORDS OR PHRASES I COMPARED TO OTHER BIBLE TRANSLATIONS:

4

CROSS REFERENCE VERSES THAT HELPED ME UNDERSTAND THIS BETTER:

5

CROSS REFERENCES CONT.

FUN FACTS I DISCOVERED:

6

LESSONS I LEARNED FROM GOD OR
THE OTHER PEOPLE:

7

THINGS I REALIZED THAT I NEED TO
CHANGE IN MY OWN LIFE:

8

PRAYER AND PRAISE BASED ON WHAT I LEARNED:

9

NOTES:

CHAPTER:

Make sure to write the verse references that correspond to your notes.

NOTES ON WHAT THIS CHAPTER IS ABOUT:

1

WHAT I READ ABOUT GOD, JESUS, HOLY SPIRIT:

2

WORDS I DEFINED:

3

WORDS OR PHRASES I COMPARED TO OTHER BIBLE TRANSLATIONS:

4

CROSS REFERENCE VERSES THAT HELPED ME UNDERSTAND THIS BETTER:

5

CROSS REFERENCES CONT.

FUN FACTS I DISCOVERED:

6

LESSONS I LEARNED FROM GOD OR
THE OTHER PEOPLE:

7

THINGS I REALIZED THAT I NEED TO
CHANGE IN MY OWN LIFE:

8

PRAYER AND PRAISE BASED ON WHAT I LEARNED:

9

NOTES:

CHAPTER:

Make sure to write the verse references that correspond to your notes.

NOTES ON WHAT THIS CHAPTER IS ABOUT:

1

WHAT I READ ABOUT GOD, JESUS, HOLY SPIRIT:

2

WORDS I DEFINED:

3

WORDS OR PHRASES I COMPARED TO OTHER BIBLE TRANSLATIONS:

4

CROSS REFERENCE VERSES THAT HELPED ME UNDERSTAND THIS BETTER:

5

CROSS REFERENCES CONT.

FUN FACTS I DISCOVERED:

6

LESSONS I LEARNED FROM GOD OR THE OTHER PEOPLE:

7

THINGS I REALIZED THAT I NEED TO CHANGE IN MY OWN LIFE:

8

PRAYER AND PRAISE BASED ON WHAT I LEARNED:

9

NOTES:

CHAPTER:

Make sure to write the verse references that correspond to your notes.

NOTES ON WHAT THIS CHAPTER IS ABOUT:

1

WHAT I READ ABOUT GOD, JESUS, HOLY SPIRIT:

2

WORDS I DEFINED:

3

WORDS OR PHRASES I COMPARED TO OTHER BIBLE TRANSLATIONS:

4

CROSS REFERENCE VERSES THAT HELPED ME UNDERSTAND THIS BETTER:

5

CROSS REFERENCES CONT.

FUN FACTS I DISCOVERED:

6

LESSONS I LEARNED FROM GOD OR THE OTHER PEOPLE:

7

THINGS I REALIZED THAT I NEED TO CHANGE IN MY OWN LIFE:

8

PRAYER AND PRAISE BASED ON WHAT I LEARNED:

9

NOTES:

CHAPTER:

Make sure to write the verse references that correspond to your notes.

NOTES ON WHAT THIS CHAPTER IS ABOUT:

1

WHAT I READ ABOUT GOD, JESUS, HOLY SPIRIT:

2

WORDS I DEFINED:

3

WORDS OR PHRASES I COMPARED TO OTHER BIBLE TRANSLATIONS:

4

CROSS REFERENCE VERSES THAT HELPED ME UNDERSTAND THIS BETTER:

5

CROSS REFERENCES CONT.

FUN FACTS I DISCOVERED:

6

LESSONS I LEARNED FROM GOD OR
THE OTHER PEOPLE:

7

THINGS I REALIZED THAT I NEED TO
CHANGE IN MY OWN LIFE:

8

PRAYER AND PRAISE BASED ON WHAT I LEARNED:

9

NOTES:

CHAPTER:

Make sure to write the verse references that correspond to your notes.

NOTES ON WHAT THIS CHAPTER IS ABOUT:

1

WHAT I READ ABOUT GOD, JESUS, HOLY SPIRIT:

2

WORDS I DEFINED:

3

WORDS OR PHRASES I COMPARED TO
OTHER BIBLE TRANSLATIONS:

4

CROSS REFERENCE VERSES THAT HELPED ME UNDERSTAND THIS BETTER:

5

CROSS REFERENCES CONT.

FUN FACTS I DISCOVERED:

6

LESSONS I LEARNED FROM GOD OR THE OTHER PEOPLE:

7

THINGS I REALIZED THAT I NEED TO CHANGE IN MY OWN LIFE:

8

PRAYER AND PRAISE BASED ON WHAT I LEARNED:

9

NOTES:

CHATPER:

Make sure to write the verse references that correspond to your notes.

NOTES ON WHAT THIS CHAPTER IS ABOUT:

1

WHAT I READ ABOUT GOD, JESUS, HOLY SPIRIT:

2

WORDS I DEFINED:

3

WORDS OR PHRASES I COMPARED TO OTHER BIBLE TRANSLATIONS:

4

CROSS REFERENCE VERSES THAT HELPED ME UNDERSTAND THIS BETTER:

5

CROSS REFERENCES CONT.

FUN FACTS I DISCOVERED:

6

LESSONS I LEARNED FROM GOD OR
THE OTHER PEOPLE:

7

THINGS I REALIZED THAT I NEED TO
CHANGE IN MY OWN LIFE:

8

PRAYER AND PRAISE BASED ON WHAT I LEARNED:

9

NOTES:

CHAPTER:

Make sure to write the verse references that correspond to your notes.

NOTES ON WHAT THIS CHAPTER IS ABOUT:

WHAT I READ ABOUT GOD, JESUS, HOLY SPIRIT:

1

2

WORDS I DEFINED:

3

WORDS OR PHRASES I COMPARED TO OTHER BIBLE TRANSLATIONS:

4

CROSS REFERENCE VERSES THAT HELPED ME UNDERSTAND THIS BETTER:

5

CROSS REFERENCES CONT.

FUN FACTS I DISCOVERED:

6

LESSONS I LEARNED FROM GOD OR
THE OTHER PEOPLE:

7

THINGS I REALIZED THAT I NEED TO
CHANGE IN MY OWN LIFE:

8

PRAYER AND PRAISE BASED ON WHAT I LEARNED:

9

NOTES:

CHAPTER:

Make sure to write the verse references that correspond to your notes.

NOTES ON WHAT THIS CHAPTER IS ABOUT:

1

WHAT I READ ABOUT GOD, JESUS, HOLY SPIRIT:

2

WORDS I DEFINED:

3

WORDS OR PHRASES I COMPARED TO OTHER BIBLE TRANSLATIONS:

4

CROSS REFERENCE VERSES THAT HELPED ME UNDERSTAND THIS BETTER:

5

CROSS REFERENCES CONT.

FUN FACTS I DISCOVERED:

6

LESSONS I LEARNED FROM GOD OR
THE OTHER PEOPLE:

7

THINGS I REALIZED THAT I NEED TO
CHANGE IN MY OWN LIFE:

8

PRAYER AND PRAISE BASED ON WHAT I LEARNED:

9

NOTES:

CHAPTER:

Make sure to write the verse references that correspond to your notes.

NOTES ON WHAT THIS CHAPTER IS ABOUT:

1

WHAT I READ ABOUT GOD, JESUS, HOLY SPIRIT:

2

WORDS I DEFINED:

3

WORDS OR PHRASES I COMPARED TO OTHER BIBLE TRANSLATIONS:

4

CROSS REFERENCE VERSES THAT HELPED ME UNDERSTAND THIS BETTER:

5

CROSS REFERENCES CONT.

FUN FACTS I DISCOVERED:

6

LESSONS I LEARNED FROM GOD OR
THE OTHER PEOPLE:

7

THINGS I REALIZED THAT I NEED TO
CHANGE IN MY OWN LIFE:

8

PRAYER AND PRAISE BASED ON WHAT I LEARNED:

9

NOTES:

CHAPTER:

Make sure to write the verse references that correspond to your notes.

NOTES ON WHAT THIS CHAPTER IS ABOUT:

1

WHAT I READ ABOUT GOD,
JESUS, HOLY SPIRIT:

2

WORDS I DEFINED:

3

WORDS OR PHRASES I COMPARED TO OTHER BIBLE TRANSLATIONS:

4

CROSS REFERENCE VERSES THAT HELPED ME UNDERSTAND THIS BETTER:

5

CROSS REFERENCES CONT.

FUN FACTS I DISCOVERED:

6

LESSONS I LEARNED FROM GOD OR
THE OTHER PEOPLE:

7

THINGS I REALIZED THAT I NEED TO
CHANGE IN MY OWN LIFE:

8

PRAYER AND PRAISE BASED ON WHAT I LEARNED:

9

NOTES: